To

From

A father is a man who car

heal most things with a hug.

I must thank you
for all you have given me.
Your laughter, your patience,
your kindness,
your friendship.

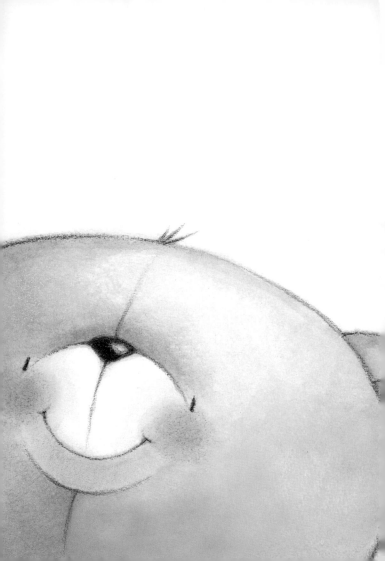

A father can be a most ordinary man made a hero by responsibility and love.

Children are inclined
to take their dad for granted.
But today I want to give you all
the thank-yous –
for all the things we did together
when I was very small –
for the laughter
and the patience
and the quiet comfort.
Thank you Dad!

Dads can make a walk
an adventure
when you are small.
It changes the way you look at life
forever.

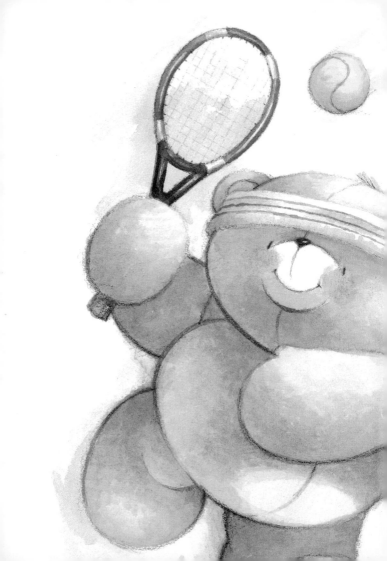

$D$ad...
you are strong and wise
and full of laughter.
Never dismiss your life
as commonplace.

Thank you for all you taught me Dad
– to look more closely,
to think more clearly,
to find joy and excitement
in the very small as well as
the very great experiences of life.

# He gives you

A father is the hands
that hold you safe.

Time passes, but your love
never falters, never fades.
You are as dear,
as necessary to my life,
as when I ran into your arms
– happy and secure.

confidence for life

$\mathrm{T}$hank you for always
being convinced
I could do anything
I set my heart on.

believed in me

It is sad when we discover
that dads can make mistakes.
But, once we are over the shock,
we see the truth.
There is a touch of magic
in a dad.
They are no longer ordinary men.

A wise father teaches skills.
Courage.
Concentration on the job in hand.
Self-discipline.
Encourages enthusiasm.
A spirit of enquiry.
Gentleness. Kindliness. Patience.
Courtesy.
And Love.

So much in our lives changes,
so many dreams don't come true.
But nothing seems to matter,
just as long as our dads love us,
and we love them.

Dads show us the wider world
for the very first time,
high on their shoulders, swaying
a little as they walk,
and lords of all creation.

Childhood is riding home,
half asleep,
on Dad's shoulders.
I'll never forget, Dad.

# We are transformed

I will love you, my dearest Dad.
Forever and forever.